The Revolutionary If.

By the same author
Maggie's Farm
Further Down on Maggie's Farm
Maggie's Farm — The Last Roundup*
The If... Chronicles*
If... Only Again*
Another Load of If...*
The Unrepeatable If...*
If... Bounces Back*
If... Breezes In*
The Vengeance of If...*

with Brian Homer
Waiting for the Upturn*

*published by Methuen

The Revolutionary If...

Steve Bell

Methuen

For Heather, William, Joe, Patrick and Katherine

This collection first published in Great Britain in 1990
by Methuen London
Michelin House, 81 Fulham Road, London SW3 6RB

The strips first published by *The Guardian* in 1989 and 1990

Copyright © Steve Bell 1989, 1990

Designed by Brian Homer

Production by Charlotte Tucker and Andy Coyne

Edited by Steve Bell and Brian Homer

Typeset by P & W Typesetters
1489 Pershore Road, Stirchley, Birmingham

Printed and bound in Great Britain
by Richard Clay Ltd, Bungay, Suffolk

ISBN 0 413 63840 5

A CIP catalogue record for this book
is available from the British Library

THE SEASONALLY ADJUSTED GLOBAL WARMING CALENDAR

JUNE

© Steve Bell 1989

YOU CAN SAY WHAT YOU LIKE ABOUT THEM CHINESE, BUT THEY CERTAINLY KNOW 'OW TO DEAL WITH THEIR 'IPPIE PROBLEM!

THASSA BIT **EXTREME**, MA!! THEY WEREN'T DOIN' ANY DAMAGE OR ANYTHING.... BESIDES — THERE WAS **MILLIONS** OF 'EM!!

CHEW CRUNCH

· 12·6·2147·

I DON'T GIVE A MONKEYS 'OW MANY THERE WERE — 'IPPIES IS 'IPPIES THE WORLD OVER, AND THEY GOTTA BE **STOPPED**!!

I THINK YOU'RE MAKIN' A MISTAKE 'ERE, MA!!

SNORT

KLIK

I THINK IN POLITICAL TERMS YOU IS MAKIN' A MISTAKEN COMPARISON BETWEEN CHINESE STUDENTS AND BRITISH 'IPPIES!

I WON'T 'AVE NO TALKIN' POLITICS IN THIS 'OUSE, YOU 'EAR?

RRR

© Steve Bell '89

LISTEN 'ERE, YOU DEWY-EYED **DUPE**!!! CHINESE 'IPPIES CHANTIN' "**FREEDOM** AN' **DEMOCRACY**"...

?

...AN' BRITISH 'IPPIES CHANTIN' "PEACE AN' LOVE"..... IT'S ALL THE BLOODY **SAME**...

13·6·2150

...AN' IT'S ALL **BOLLOCKS**!!! NONE OF 'EM'S DONE A DAYS WORK IN THEIR LIVES!!

URR'S NO NEED TO USE PROFANITY, MOTHER!

Panel 1: 'ERE, MOTHER—THAT'S THE **BULL** YOU'M MILKIN' THERE!!!

Panel 2: YOU THINK I'M **STUPID**, DON'T 'EE, MISTER BLOODY CLEVER CLOGS—BUT YOU'RE **WRONG!** THIS'ERE IS THE **PEAK OF FARMIN' EFFICIENCY!**

Panel 3: ...MY **EURO-HORMONE SUBSIDY CHEQUE** ENABLES ME TO **BOOST** MILK YIELD IN AS YET UNEXPLOITED AREAS. TEN YEARS AGO THIS BULL PRODUCED **NO MILK AT ALL.** TODAY IT'S PRODUCIN' **THREE GALLON A WEEK!!**

Panel 4: THAT'S AN INCREASE OF **INFINITY PER CENT!!** AN' IF THE BULL KEEPS IT UP LONG ENOUGH WITHOUT GOIN' ROUND THE BEND, THEY'LL **PAY ME T' STOP DOIN' IT!!** THASS **EFFICIENCY,** BOY!!

CRANK CLANK

Panel 5: MABEL!! 'URRY IT UP!! WE'M 'UNGRY!! TIS 'UNGRY WORK WRASSLIN' SCHIZOID GENDER-BENDER BATT'RY PIGLETS ALL DAY!

RRRP

Panel 6: MABEL! AIN'T YOU FED MY BOYS YET? 'URRY IT UP, GIRL!! 'AVE YOU BOYS **VOTED** YET??

YURR! I VOTED **DEMOCRAT** COS I'M SICK O' POLITICS!

RRRR

Panel 7: YURRR!! I VOTED **LABOUR** 'COS I LIKE THEIR NEW SICK O' POLITICS IMAGE!!

YURR! I VOTED **SIR JASPER** 'COS I KNOW MY **PLACE** AN' I ADMIRE A MAN 'OO KNOWS 'IS **ALSATIAN WINES!**

Panel 8: I DON'T GO FOR THEM WHININ' ALSATIANS! I'M A **ROTTWEILER PERSON** MESELF SO I VOTED **SDP!!** 'OW 'BOUT **YOU,** MABEL?

I **DIDN'T VOTE**—THE WHOLE BUSINESS IS **IRRELEVANT!**

NO MABEL—IT'S NOT AN **ELEPHANT**—ISSA **ROTTWEILER!**

RRRR

8

YOU DON'T MEAN TO TELL ME YOU VOTED **GREEN** DID YOU MABEL?? I TOLD YOU—I DIDN'T VOTE ANYTHING! THE WHOLE BUSINESS IS **IRRELEVANT**!

THANK **GAHD** FOR THAT!! I COULDN'T 'AVE NO **DAUGHTER** O'MINE VOTIN' FOR THE 'IPPIE PARTY'!!

'DAUGHTER'??! —I THOUGHT MABEL WAS THE **AU PAIR**, MA!

© Steve Bell 1989

NO, NO, MA—THE GREENS ARE ALL VERY **NICE** AN' WELL MEANING AN' ECO-FRIENDLY AN' THAT, BUT THEY **AIN'T GOT NO** POLITICS!

I WON'T 'AVE **POLITICS** DISCUSSED IN THIS 'OUSE, YOU 'EAR ME??

16·6·2153—

BOOMP

I MEAN—WHERE DO THEY STAND IN RELATION TO THE LEGITIMATE **MATERIAL** AND **ANTI-IMPERIALIST** STRUGGLE OF THE GLOBAL **WORKING CLASS**, MA??

MABEL—DON'T YOU TALK T'ME 'BOUT **LEGITIMATE**. YOU AIN'T **LEGITIMATE**, SO **KEEP YOUR MOUTH SHUT**!!

RRRR

GRRRR!! THE **ROTTWEILER SUBSIDY CHEQUE** IS DOWN THIS MONTH! I'M GONNA COMPLAIN TO **BRUSSELS**!!

I'M GONNA HAFTA **GET RID** O'SOME O'YOU BUGGERS IF THIS GOES ON!! **DRIED YOOMAN LEGS** COST **BIG MONEY** THESE DAYS!

I MEAN, WHY DO I **BOTHER** WITH ALL THIS **FUSSIN'** ABOUT? IS IT WORTH THE 'EARTACHE AN' THE **WORRY**??

© Steve Bell '89

RRRR RIP GRRR SNORT

WHY SHOULD I WASTE ME TIME PRESERVIN' OUR RURAL 'ERITAGE FOR POSTERITY? WHAT'S POSTERITY EVER DONE FOR ME??

17·6·2154—

ROTTWEILER SLURRY ANTI-FOOTPATH SPRAY

THE LAW LORDS PONDER:

NOW I'M GOING TO SUMMARISE THE PORT EMPLOYERS' POSITION: SHOOT ME DOWN IN FLAMES IF YOU THINK I'M TALKING OUT MY ARSE:

BY THE WAY: COULD YOU OPEN A WINDOW, COLIN – IT'S HOT AS HELL IN HERE AND I THINK DES HERE HAS JUST DROPPED ONE...

NO WAY, JOHN!!

IF WE MAY JUST DIGRESS AT THIS POINT: COULD WE HAVE A SHOW OF HANDS? ALL THOSE WHO THINK DES IS THE GUILTY ONE?

ALL THOSE WHO THINK IT WAS SOMEBODY ELSE? SORRY DES – THERE'S NO APPEAL AGAINST THIS ONE. WE ARE THE ULTIMATE, Y'KNOW. NOW WHERE WERE WE.....?

19.6.2155

IN A NUTSHELL, THE PORT EMPLOYERS' ARGUMENT IS THIS: THE TERMS OF THE NATIONAL DOCK LABOUR SCHEME CONSTITUTE A NO-STRIKE AGREEMENT...

..THEREFORE, SINCE THE DOCK LABOUR SCHEME STILL EXISTS TECHNICALLY SPEAKING UNTIL THE ACTUAL MOMENT OF ITS ABOLITION, THERE IS NO RIGHT TO STRIKE IN THE DOCKS AT THIS PRECISE MOMENT IN TIME...

...THEREFORE THE T. & G. MUST FORFEIT VAST AMOUNTS OF MONEY SINCE IT HAS BEEN OPERATING ILLEGALLY SINCE 1946. HOW DOES THAT GRAB YOU?

NNNN

NNNN

ARK ARK!!

20.6.2156

IT SEEMS TO ME THAT MORE MONEY FOR PORT EMPLOYERS MEANS MORE, BETTER, CHEAPER AND MORE FREQUENT PORT. YES, I THINK WE OUGHT TO GO WITH THIS ONE.

BANG BANG

10

AHHH YES — I'M JUST BEING HANDED A **MEMO** HERE: IT SEEMS WE'VE BEEN LABOURING UNDER A BIT OF A **MIS-APPREHENSION**...

21-6-2·57

...THE PORT EMPLOYERS HAVE ABSOLUTELY **NO CONNECTION** WITH THE WELL KNOWN **FORTIFIED BEVERAGE**...

WELL *☆*∂'EM THEN!!

YEAH! *@*'EM! GIVE THE DOCKERS A **BREAK**!!

© Steve Bell 1989

...APART FROM THEIR OBVIOUS CONNECTION WITH ANY IMPORTED COMMODITY...

LET 'EM HAVE A BIT OF A **STRIKE**! WE'RE **BROAD MINDED**, YEAH!!

...WHICH MEANS A DOCK STRIKE COULD HAVE A **VERY DISRUPTIVE EFFECT** ON **PORT SUPPLIES**

LET ME RE-PHRASE: THE **NATIONAL INTEREST** IS **THREATENED**; SMASH THE T. & G.!!!

I ECHO THESE SENTIMENTS WHOLE-HEARTEDLY!

OKAY: WE'VE GOT A **VERDICT**! "LAW LORDS SAY: **TOUGH TITTY, RON**: YOU AND YOUR **BOLSHIE BULLY BOYS** ARE IN A **NO-WIN** SITUATION WITH REGARD TO THIS ONE!"

HANG ON A MINUTE!

22·6·2·58

© Steve Bell 1989

WHAT'S THE **PROBLEM**, COL??

FAIRLY CRUCIAL POINT HERE, JOHN, VIS-À-VIS THE PROTEST MEASURES AGAINST THE **LORD CHANCELLOR'S LEGAL REFORMS**.....

SHAG A PARROT!! I FORGOT WE WERE ON A **GO-SLOW**! WE'LL **SIT** ON THIS VERDICT TILL WE SEE SOME SHIFT FROM THE **SCOTCH GIT**!!

11

AT A PROTRACTED SITTING OF THE **LAW LORDS:**

WHAT ABOUT THIS EURO BUSINESS, EH?

YOU TALKING ABOUT THE **EURO-ELECTION** OR ABOUT THE **EUROPEAN COURT OF HUMAN RIGHTS** AND WHETHER IT TAKES **PRECEDENCE** OVER **US??**

NAH

NAH, I DON'T GIVE A MONKEY'S ABOUT THAT — WHAT I'M WORRIED ABOUT IS MORE **PROCEDURAL**....

OH YEAH

NO WAY AM I GONNA WEAR A **ROUND HAT** WITH A **FLAT TOP!!**

WHAT **DO** THEY THINK THEY **LOOK** LIKE?

SCOTCH GIT OUT

JUDGES ARE WORKING TO RULE

SAVE THE WIG

WIGS IN DANGER

WAKE UP, COL— IT'S THE **MEDIA!!!**

JUDGE ARE WORKING TO RULE

SAVE THE WIG

WE'RE **SOLID** BARRY!!

NO WAY IS OUR CAMPAIGN TO SAVE THE WIG MOTIVATED BY **SELFISH INERTIA**

ALL OUT BEAK STRIKE NOW

SAVE THE WIG

THE FACT OF THE MATTER IS JUDGES' HEADGEAR REQUIREMENTS KEEP **FIVE HUNDRED SHEEP** USEFULLY EMPLOYED ACROSS THE NATION!

ALL OUT BEAK STRIKE NOW

12

DEEP UNDER **FORTRESS WILTSHIRE**

WHAT HAVE YOU **DONE** BEWIGGED **SCUMBAG**??

I...I...ER...

26·6·2161—

WE ARE **NOT BEST PLEASED** WITH YOUR DECISION ON THE **DOCKERS**!

IT WAS A **MISTAKE**, MAJESTY!

HOW SO? WIRES GOT CROSSED MA'AM; **DES** TOLD **COL** THAT **I** WAS ANNOUN-CING THE DECISION; I THOUGHT **COL** WAS, THEN **LES** TALKED TO THE **MEDIA**....

©Steve Bell 1989

...IT WASN'T HIS **FAULT**, MAJESTY— IT WAS THE **PORT** TALKING.... HE'D HAD A **BUSY** DAY...HAY FEVER....SUMMER COLD... ...**AAARRRGHHH! NO!!** NOT THE **WIG!!** DON'T CHOP THE **WIG!!!** AïEEEEEEE!!! AïEEEEEEE!!

SNIP SNAP

DEEP IN **FORTRESS WILTSHIRE:**

AHT YOU GO, TRAITAH!!

OH MY GOD! YIN YIN YIN!!

27·6·2162

BOOMF

OWOWOWOWOW OWOWOOOO THE SHAME OF IT!!

©Steve Bell 1989

SUSPECTED DEMON DRUID AT 12 O'CLOCK: COMMENCE SNATCH PROCEDURE!

POP POP POP POP POP

LURCH

LURCH

SHUFFLE SHUFFLE

13

NAH THEN NAH THEN, DRUID FEATURES! WE DON'T LIKE YOUR APPEARANCE SO WE'RE RUNNIN' YOU AHT O' WILTSHIRE UNDER THE TERMS OF THE PUBLIC ORDER ACT!!

BUT... ...BUT...

28-6-2163

..BUT I'M A LAW LORD!! I'M SUPPOSED TO LOOK LIKE THIS!! I DEMAND THAT YOU PUT ME DOWN!

? 'E SLIPPED AHTA ME GRASP! 'E'S GETTIN' AWAY!!

© Steve Bell 1989—

SORRY MILORD! —OUR MISTAKE!

DEEP IN A BUNKER IN WILTS:

GUMBUM! DID I HEAR SOMEBODY SAY "RESHUFFLE"?

© Steve Bell 1989—

DO I STILL HEAR THAT WORD, E'EN THROUGH TEN FEET OF LEADLINED CONCRETE?? DID YOU SAY THAT WORD, LITTLE GUMBOIL??

I WISH ONLY TO DO THY WILL ON EARTH, HOLINESS!

GUMBOIL...DEAR, DEAR LOYAL GUMGUM....SHALL I MAKE YOU.....ARCHBISHOP, LITTLE GUMMER? FOREIGN SECRETARY?? CHANCELLOR OF THE DUCHY OF LANCASTER? LORD PRIVY SEAL?? FIRST SEA LORD??

YOU DO ME TOO GREAT AN HONOUR MA'AM!!

...OR SHALL I SQUEEZE YOUR NASTY PINK LITTLE HEAD TILL IT BURSTS LIKE A BAG OF CUSTARD??

29-6-2164

14

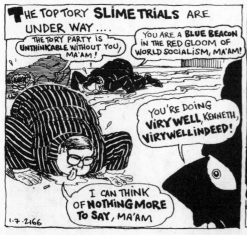

Panel 1:

A MEETING OF THE EUROPEAN DOG HARMONISATION SUB COMMITTEE .....

EUREKA!

COMMENT?

QUE?

HOCH?

NNNN?

"I have found it!" (You what?)

Panel 2:

MIO IL **EURO-HUND** NUEVA TROVO IN KEBABHAUS BAÑAÑA HUBLA **HUBLA**; JØPPA JØPPA HEY HEY ....

"T the **EURO-HOUND** have found... (sorry - I couldn't quite get the last bit ...er...)

Panel 3:

SI! EL EURO-POOCHO **MOLTO CHEAPO** ES!! MOINS DE **UNO E.C.U.** PAR AÑO GELD GESPENDEN!!!

BRAVO!

BRAVO!

"Yes! The **EURO-DOG** much cheap is!! Less than one **E.C. U.** per annum money costs!!"

Panel 4:

VOILÀ – LE "**POOBULLHUAHUA -WOLFWEILER**" !!!

© Steve Bell '89

Panel 5:

LE **EURO-CHIEN** "POOBULLHUA- -HUAWOLFWEILER" PUVO TRACO LUI-MÊME VON VASTO LANGEN KILOMETRES...

The Euro-Dog "POOBULLHUAHUA WOLFWEILER" can track itself down over huge distances...

Panel 6:

..HABLO BUENAVISTA BOOLL DOGUE, INTELLIGENZ ALSATIEN RUMPA, BLITZ KRIEG VON CHIHUAHUA, POMPADORO QUIFFÅ STYLISMØ....

...It has the good looks of a Bulldog, the intelligence of the rear end of an Alsatian, the killing power of a Chihuahua and the hairstyle of a Poodle.

Panel 7:

MANGEA CARTONA A BAMB- -INO MINO; SCHEISSE DUPLO; PONCHO HONCHO JEDENTAG ...

...It eats anything from a cardboard box to a medium sized child, and can excrete more than twice its own weight daily.

Panel 8:

CROYO ULTIMO CANOAUTO - SNUFF AL MUNDO CHERCHEZ DE EUROP TIEMPO IMMEMORALE.

© Steve Bell 1989

We believe it to be the ultim- ate deterrent against cats and Public Servants that Europe is crying out for.

THE SEASONALLY ADJUSTED GLOBAL WARMING CALENDAR

JULY

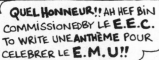

19

THIS IS **BLAIR BOLLOCKS** IN THE **BBC RADIO CAR** SOMEWHERE ON THE ROAD INTO CENTRAL LONDON HANDING YOU BACK TO **BETTY BLIP** US IN BROADCASTING HOUSE.

10·7·2173

THANKS BLAIR. THAT SOUNDS PRETTY BAD. NOW, LET'S GO OVER TO **BARRY BLOCKHEAD** IN ANOTHER BBC RADIO CAR. WHAT'S THE POSITION, BARRY??

ON THE AIR

IT'S **BLOODY ATROCIOUS**, BETTY ....BUT I DON'T QUITE UNDERSTAND YOUR CONCERN. THIS IS A **NORMAL MONDAY** — THE RAIL STRIKE'S NOT ON TILL **WEDNESDAY**!

BOGGLER BOGGLER

I BEG YOUR PARDON?? OH... AHH..... ERR........ NOW IT'S TIME FOR '**THOUGHT FOR THE DAY**' SO IT'S OVER TO **MULLAH MAX RAFSANJANI**.

THANK YOU, BETTY.

©Steve Bell '89

AS I WAS SITTING IN A **TAXI** ON MY WAY TO BROADCASTING HOUSE THIS MORNING I THOUGHT: "WHAT ON **EARTH** AM I GOING TO SAY TO THE **GREAT BRITISH TRAVELLING PUBLIC**??"

11·7·2174

MAX MULLAH

...HOW WILL THEY RESPOND TO HAVING A **MAD MULLAH**, ALBEIT A MODERATELY MAD ONE, **SOUNDING OFF** ABOUT ALL AND SUNDRY WHILE THEY SIT AND FUME....

...THEN I THOUGHT: '**SO WHAT?**' BECAUSE THAT'S ONE OF THE **JOYS** OF BEING A MAD MULLAH: **WHAT YOU SAY GOES.** ANYBODY SAYS DIFFERENT: **SKKRRLLLKKK... WALLOP!!!**

©Steve Bell 1989

...KNOW WHAT I MEAN?? **RELIGION!!** WHERE WOULD **I** BE WITHOUT IT? DO **YOU** KNOW? DOES **ANYBODY** KNOW?? DOES **ANYBODY** SER-IOUSLY GIVE A **MONKEYS**?? KEEP YOUR **NOSE CLEAN**; DON'T TAKE ANY **WOODEN MONEY**; MIND HOW Y'GO; **ALLAH BE SEEIN' YEW** ♫ ♪ IN ALL THE OL' FAMILIAR ♫ ♪ ♪ **PLACES** ♫ ♪ ♪

IT'S THIRTEEN AND A HALF MINUTES PAST EIGHT...

21

THIS IS **BLAIRBOLLOCKS** IN THE **BBC RADIO CAR** SOMEWHERE ON THE ROAD INTO CENTRAL LONDON, AND IT'S **ABSOLUTE CHAOS** HERE, BETTY.... ...I'VE JUST SEEN **THREE OLD LADIES DIE**!....

BOGGLER BOGGLER

12·7·2175

WAS THAT A **DIRECT RESULT** OF THE **NALGO ACTION**, BLAIR?

NO, NO.T.. EXACTLY....

WAS IT THE **RAILMEN**, BLAIR? WAS IT **DIRECTLY CONSEQUENT** UPON ACTIONS TAKEN BY STRIKING MEMBERS OF THE **NATIONAL UNION OF RAILWAYMEN** ??

ERRR....IT'S HARD TO SAY, BETTY ...THAT MIGHT BE **STRETCHING IT** JUST A TEENSY BIT...

....I DID ACTUALLY RUN THE OLD BATS DOWN MYSELF —BUT YOU COULD SAY **I MYSELF** AM HERE AS A **DIRECT RESULT** OF THE **N.U.R. ACTION!**

IT'S SIXTEEN MINUTES PAST EIGHT....

LET'S URP ZERE ARE **NURR COCK** URPS WEEZ MA BILLION FRONC PAGEANT **RÉVOLUTIONNAIRE**!!

'OOO RAH!!

13·7·2176 —

.... AVEC **SON**, **LUMIÈRE**, LE **BOUM·BOUM**, LE **SMELL**, LE **TASTE**, LE **FEEL TOTALE**....

MONSIEUR L'ARTISTE

...WEEZ MURST EVAIR **LAZAIRE BIM** IN 'ISTOIRE DU MONDE... ...SEE...I **PLOOCK** ZEM LARK THE **STRURNGS** OF ZE 'AARRRP !!!

VOMPEDA VOMPEDA VOMPEDA VOMPEDA VOMPEDA BING BONG BEEBEEEP BIP BOP BOP

URPS! PARDONNEZ MOI, MONSIEUR LE PRÉSIDENT !!

OUF!

24

MY **OFFICIAL INFORMATION BUREAU**, MADE UP OF THE THREE **FATTEST RATS** IN THE UNIVERSE, WILL GIVE YOU THE **FACTS**!

19·7·2181

FACT: **90%** OF BRITISH RIVERS ARE CLASSIFIED AS "QUITE TO FAIRLY LONG"!

FACT: URBAN SMOKE CONCENTRATIONS HAVE FALLEN **SIXFOLD** SINCE THE ABOLITION OF CHOO CHOOS!!..

FACT: I STOPPED PICKING MY NOSE IN **1983**!

© STEVE BELL 1989

RIDLEY, YOU **SCOUNDREL**!! WHAT ABOUT ALL THESE **RATS AND TURDS**??

-20·7·2182-

THE **RATS** ARE TESTING THE WATER **SCIENTIFICALLY**...

WIPE OUT!!

...AND IF YOU BELIEVE THAT YOU'LL BELIEVE ANYTHING! **MUGS!! SUCKERS!!!** SCIENTIFICALLY, THERE'S ONLY **ONE WAY** TO DEAL WITH A SERIOUS ENVIRON- MENTAL **RODENT EXPLOSION**

© STEVE BELL '89

VOTE CONSERVATIVE AND SUMMON UP THE **PIED POOPER**!!! CACKLE CACKLE!!

27

THE SEASONALLY ADJUSTED GLOBAL WARMING CALENDAR

AUGUST

Meet the VEGETABLES

No. 3: JOHN SELWYN CUCUMBER VEGETABLE OF STATE FOR AGRICULTURE

2·8·2193

COO! INCREASE **PUBLIC CONFIDENCE** IN **AGRIBIZ**, AND IN **BRAIN-DISEASED MOOCOW** LYSTERIA AND **SALMONELLA** PRODUCTION. THAT'S A **TOUGH TASK** FOR A **GREENHOUSE FRUIT**!!

SHE OBVIOUSLY WANTED **ME** BECAUSE, BEING A **VEGETABLE** I HAVE **UNIQUE INSIGHT** INTO THE SUBJECT, ISN'T THAT SO, MA'AM ???

© Steve Bell '89

NOT AT ALL — I CHOSE YOU BECAUSE YOU'RE THE NEAREST THING TO A **COMPLETE DICK** THE VEGETABLE KINGDOM HAS **YET** PRODUCED!

HRRMMMM

BLUSH
BLUSH

— 3·8·2194 —

"ICH BIN EIN POLISHER"...

POLAND WELCOMES THE HUMAN ZERO

ZZZZ   ZZZZ

YIPPEEYI - YAWNSKI!

"ASK **NOT** WHAT **YOUR COUNTRY** CAN DO FOR **YOU**, ASK WHAT **YOU** CAN DO FOR **YOUR COUNTRY**..."

DODGE CITY WELCOMES MR MYSTERY

HOW ABOUT **30 YEARS** IN THE PENITENTIARY?

I **PLEDGE** THAT THIS ADMINISTRATION WILL COMMIT **RESOURCES** TOWARD THE **ACHIEVEMENT**..

STARWARBURG WELCOMES PRESIDENT BUSH

© Steve Bell 1989

...OF GETTING A **HEAVILY ARMED MAN** TO **MARS** BEFORE THE END OF THIS **MILLENIUM**!

STARWAR WELCOMES PRESIDENT BUSH

CHARISMA CHARISMAA!!

CHARISMAA CHARISMAAGH!

33

TO MARS BY STEALTH BOMBER! WHAT A KEEN IDEA!!

4·8·2195·

SAVES MONEY — LESS NOISE, MORE ENVIRONMENTALLY FRIENDLY...

TO BOLDLY GO NOWHERE WHERE NO MAN HAS GONE BEFORE...

© Steve Bell 1989

...TO SEEK OUT NEW WORLDS AND DROP BIG ONES ON THEM

IN A DESPERATE BID TO GAIN CHARISMA AND SUBSTANCE, GEORGE BUSH PLANS TO BE THE FIRST HEAVILY ARMED MAN ON MARS:

QUACK QUACK BEEP QUACK

BEEP

5·8·2196·

HEY! I'VE JUST HAD ANOTHER NEATO IDEA!!

WHILE I'M UP HERE I CAN TRY OUT SOME OF THAT STAR WARS TECHNOLOGY!!

WHADDYA KNOW!! NONE OF IT WORKS!!! GUESS WE NEED TO PUT A LITTLE MORE RESOURCES INTO IT!! HOW 'BOUT THAT?? HOUSTON: HOW'S MY CHARISMA LEVEL???

BEEP

© Steve Bell 1989

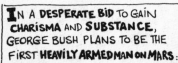

35

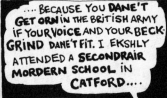

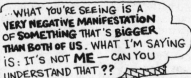

THE SEASONALLY ADJUSTED GLOBAL WARMING CALENDAR

SEPTEMBER

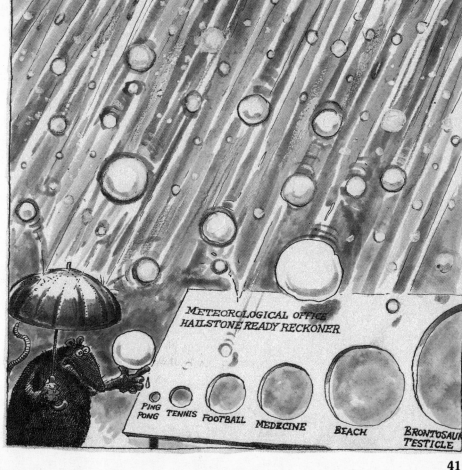

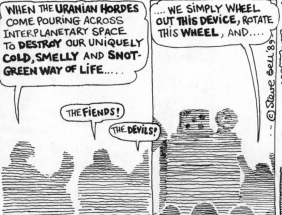

45

46

47

50

NOW IN ORDER TO FILL OUT THIS H_2O OWNERSHIP APPLICATION ON YOUR BEHALF, I MUST KNOW WHETHER YOU ARE RECEIVING BOTH WATER AND SEWERAGE SERVICES FROM US, OR DO YOU RECEIVE ONLY ONE OF THESE SERVICES??

ER...

WELL, I SWIM IN IT, AND I CRAP IN IT, AND I GENERALLY EXIST IN IT AS IT WERE.....

COO! DO FISH ACTUALLY CRAP?

WHAT DO YOU TAKE ME FOR?? I'M A CREATURE! I'M A MEMBER OF THE ANIMAL KINGDOM — OF COURSE I CRAP!!

WELL YOU LIVE AND LEARN! I'LL PUT YOU DOWN FOR BOTH, THEN!

©Steve Bell 1989

OI! — WHAT ABAHT MY SPECIAL INCENTIVES??

AAAH!

23-9-2226 -

GLAD YOU ASKED ME THAT — ALL SUBMARINE H_2O OWNERS GET AS MUCH WATER AS THEY CAN DRINK... UNTIL WE START METERING IT....

©Steve Bell '89

..A CONSTANT SUPPLY OF THESE UNIQUE TEAR-OFF TOILET VOUCHERS..

...AND DID I MENTION THE UNLIMITED FREE CONDOMS??

51

52

THE SEASONALLY ADJUSTED GLOBAL WARMING CALENDAR

OCTOBER

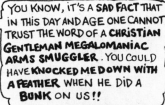

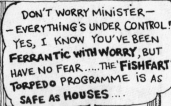

DON'T WORRY MINISTER—EVERYTHING'S UNDER CONTROL! YES, I KNOW YOU'VE BEEN **FERRANTIC** WITH WORRY, BUT HAVE NO FEAR.....THE 'FISHFART' TORPEDO PROGRAMME IS AS SAFE AS HOUSES....

29·9·2231·

...OUR NEW PRODUCT RANGE HAS SOME ABSOLUTE **WORLD BEATERS**! AND TO CAP IT ALL WE HAVE SOMETHING THAT **NOBODY** ELSE HAS GOT :

THE WORLD'S FIRST "GREEN" MISSILE!! WHAT'S THAT, YOU MAY WELL ASK, SIR....

...IT'S EXACTLY THE SAME AS **ANY OTHER MISSILE**, EXCEPT THAT WE PAINT IT GREEN AND SELL IT AT A **HUNDRED PERCENT MARK UP**!!

WHACKO!

PHOSPHATE FREE

© Steve Bell '89

MINISTER — I REGRET TO SAY THAT OUR RECENTLY ACQUIRED "ASSET HOLE" HAS LEFT US RATHER EXPOSED TO FOREIGN TAKEOVER.....

I BEG YOUR PARDON?

30·9·2232·

...I DON'T WANT TO WORRY YOU, AND YOU CAN **REST ASSURED** THAT THE 'FISHFART' PROGRAMME AND THE ALL-THINKING, ALL-SEEING, ALL-DANCING **CLUSTER BOMBLET** ARE BOTH AS SAFE AS HOUSES.....

©Steve Bell 1989—

...I SHOULD TELL YOU THAT WE'VE HAD A COUPLE OF **VERY GOOD** OFFERS FROM **HIGHLY REPUTABLE COMPANIES**....ONE FROM **KRUPPS** WHICH LOOKS **VERY PROMISING INDEED**....

...AND ONE FROM **LADA** WHICH WE'RE NOT ENTIRELY SURE ABOUT....

DE·LUXE 5 DOOR, ELECTRIC WINDOWS, POWER STEERING, STEREO WASH/WIPE, WITH FULL GUIDANCE SYSTEM

58

MAXWELL HAS SUNK BRIGHTON PIER:

HAINES — MY ACCIDENTALLY CAUSING THE SEA LEVEL TO RISE BY TEN FEET.....

...HAS MADE ME THINK AGAIN ABOUT OUR WORLD — I'M GOING GREEN!

ROGER BOSS!

GLUB!

— © Steve Bell 1989 —

6·10·2237

THAT'S RIGHT — I'M GOING GREEN WITH ENVY CONTEMPLATING THE PROFITS OF THESE 'ECO-FRIENDLY' SUPERMARKET CHAINS!

ABSOLUTELY, CHIEF!

The Brighton Centre

SAFEWAY

TESCO

Sainsbury's
ALL OUR EMPLOYEES ARE 100% BIO-DEGRADABLE

THE NEW SOCIALISM IS ABOUT REALISM, NEIL. THE BRITISH PEOPLE WANT IT AND NEED IT.....

7·10·2238

REALISM ABOUT DEFENCE: THE BRITISH PEOPLE ARE CRYING OUT FOR A SUICIDE MACHINE THAT COSTS £11 BILLION AND DOESN'T EVEN WORK.....

REALISM ABOUT THE ECONOMY: THE BRITISH PEOPLE ARE CRYING OUT FOR TOTAL FREEDOM OF CAPITAL AND FOR THE RIGHT TO BE ARBITRARILY SACKED BY PEOPLE LIKE ME.....

© Steve Bell 1989

...AND REALISM ABOUT THE ENVIRONMENT: THE BRITISH PEOPLE ARE CRYING OUT FOR RAMBO TO STEP IN AND WIPE OUT THE GREENHOUSE EFFECT!!

YOU DAMN GOOKS HAVE BIN BREATHIN' TOO MUCH AIR FER TOO LONG!

60

62

63

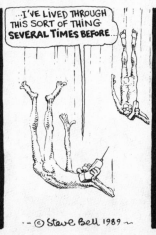

THE SEASONALLY ADJUSTED GLOBAL WARMING CALENDAR

NOVEMBER

68

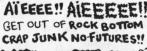

AH.... HELLO CLIENT! I'LL GIVE YOU A MARKET SITUATION UPDATE!

-27·10·2255-

...I AM NOW BEING DISEMBOWELLED BY DEMONS AS I FLOUNDER UP TO MY CHIN IN BOILING SHIT...

©Steve Bell 1989

...I THINK I MADE A MINOR MISCALCULATION BY BUYING INTO EURO-TUNNEL AT JUST THE WRONG MOMENT...... ...APART FROM THAT I'M FEELING QUITE POSITIVE ABOUT THE PROSPECTS....

...OF BEING FED TO A GIANT BRASS EFFIGY OF NIGEL LAWSON !!

WAIT! WAIT!! BEFORE YOU FEED ME TO THE BRAZEN LAWSON TOTEM, LET ME MAKE ONE LAST PHONECALL! I'VE HAD A GREAT MONEYMAKING IDEA!!

-28·10·2256-

IT'S FOR A SOAP OPERA... ..YAH! YAH! FULL OF REALLY Y'KNOW, RAUNCHY YOUNG RUBBER PEOPLE IN STRIPY SHIRTS AND HIGH CLASS DESIGNER CLOTHES.... ...FLASHY CARS...BIG MONEY. ...EVERYBODY BONKING EVERYBODY ELSE....

....AND THEN, TOTALLY UNEXPECTEDLY, THEY ALL JUMP OUT OF THE WINDOW AND END UP IN THE DEEP SHIT!! DOOM! GLOOM!! DRAMA!! THEN, THE GOVERNMENT COMES TO THE RESCUE WITH BILLIONS OF POUNDS OF PRECIOUS PUBLIC MONEY, AND THEY ALL LIVE HAPPILY EVER AFTER!! WHADDYA THINK??

BURP!

-©Steve Bell 1989-

70

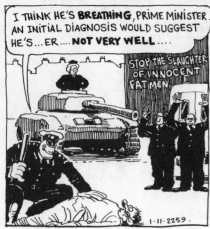

3-11-2261

SORRY MA'AM — IT WAS A **HOAX CALL** — THERE'S BEEN **NO MEGASMASH** IN THE MIDLANDS!

PAH!

YOU MEAN I'VE COME ALL THIS WAY FOR **NOTHING!?**

— © Steve Bell 1989 —

WHAT IS THIS **HELL HOLE** ANYWAY? ARE YOU **SURE** THERE HASN'T BEEN A **DISASTER** HERE? DAMN WELL LOOKS TO ME LIKE THERE HAS!

NO MA'AM — THIS IS **BIRMINGHAM!**

...IT LOOKS LIKE THIS **NATURALLY!** AHH... QUITE BRINGS BACK THE **OLD DAYS** — I USED TO BE **ON THE FORCE** HERE MA'AM!!

SO WHAT DO YOU WANT — A MEDAL?

AHH ME!! BIRMINGHAM! BIRMINGHAM!! WHAT **MEMORIES!!** THOSE BALMY DAYS ON THE CUNNINGLY NAMED '**SERIOUS CRIME SQUAD**'!!

4-11-2262

...AND I WAS PART OF THE TEAM THAT BROUGHT THE **BIRMINGHAM SIX** TO JUSTICE. DIFFICULT TIMES THEY WERE: — **TERRIBLE CRIME,** WE WERE **CLUELESS** AND WE NEEDED SOME **HANDY MICKS** TO STITCH IT ON. I THOUGHT WE DONE A **FAIR JOB**...

OK SEAMUS: THIS IS A **FIT UP!**

CONVENIENT IRISH STEREO-TYPE

© Steve Bell 89

...THE CLINCHER WAS THE **BENT FORENSIC EVIDENCE** (THAT WAS DISCREDITED YEARS AGO AND THE POOR SODS ARE **STILL** INSIDE) FWORRRGHH!! I WAS A **BAD BASTARD** IN THOSE DAYS..

OF COURSE — THAT WAS ALL A LONG TIME BEFORE I WAS "**BORN AGAIN**", MA'AM!

73

— ©Steve Bell '89 —

WHAT DO **YOU** WANT??

.ER....

WELL?? C'MON — SPIT IT OUT!!!

ERRM....WELL.. ..ER....THE FACT IS, MA'AM....

...WE'RE VERY CONCERNED ABOUT YOUR **STYLE** OF LEADERSHIP!...

HA HA HA!!!

SNORT

...SO YOU'RE CONCERNED ABOUT MY "**STYLE OF LEADERSHIP**" ARE YOU??

WHAT EXACTLY IS IT ABOUT MY "**STYLE**" THAT SO CONCERNS YOU?? **WELL??**.... **YOU** — —WHAT DO **YOU** HAVE TO SAY? **WHO ARE YOU** BY THE WAY??

UM...YES....UM... ...I AM **CRANLEY ONSLOW**, MA'AM

WELL, WELL: **DIMLY HOUNSLOW!** WHAT EXACTLY IS IT YOU OBJECT TO? IS IT MY **DRESS SENSE**?? IS IT MY **VOWEL SOUNDS**??.. ...WELL?? **WELL???**

NO...UM...YES...UM ...NO MUM....

DO YOU HAVE ANY IDEA WHAT A "**CARMEN ROLLER**" IS, YOU GHASTLY LITTLE MAN??

ER...NO, MUM...UM ...NUM......

WELL, I SUGGEST YOU GO AWAY AND FIND OUT, THEN COME BACK AND TALK TO ME ABOUT "**STYLE**"

— ©Steve Bell '89 ~

74

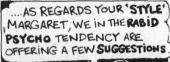

Panel 1: MARGARET....I MUST TELL YOU THAT THERE IS **CONCERN** IN THE **PARTY**....

AIEEEEEE!!!

10·11·2267

Panel 2: ...ABOUT YOUR **STYLE OF LEADERSHIP,** MARGARET

MY **STYLE?** WHAT'S WRONG WITH MY STYLE?

Panel 3: IT'S **SEMI-DETACHED,** MARGARET!!

SOD OFF NEIGHBOURS

© Steve Bell 1989

SEMI-DETACHED?? WHAT DO YOU MEAN??

Panel 4: SEMI-DETACHED FROM **REALITY**, MARGARET : THE **RABID PSYCHO WING** OF THE PARTY IS CONCERNED THAT, UNLESS YOU GO THE WHOLE HOG AND **DETACH YOURSELF UTTERLY FROM** REALITY P.D.Q., WE COULD BE **UP TOILET CREEK!!**

HMMM.....YOU COULD HAVE A POINT THERE, NORMAN...

Panel 5: ....AS REGARDS YOUR 'STYLE' MARGARET, WE IN THE **RABID PSYCHO** TENDENCY ARE OFFERING A FEW **SUGGESTIONS**

11·11·2268

Panel 6: ...HAVE YOU EVER THOUGHT OF **BLACK LEATHER CURTAINS** FOR NUMBER TEN??

MMM

© Steve Bell 89

SOD THE NEIGHBOURS

Panel 7: ...AND DID YOU KNOW THAT **JODHPURS** ARE REALLY **"IN"** AT THE MOMENT -- SO HOW ABOUT DRESSING UP THE **ENTIRE CABINET** IN THEM?!

MMMM....LIKE IT, **LIKE IT!!**

Panel 8: **THANK YOU,** NORMAN - OUR LITTLE TALK HAS BEEN MOST USEFUL. I REALLY FEEL WE COULD BE **ON OUR WAY** AT LAST!

SOD THE NEIGHBOUR

10

THE SEASONALLY ADJUSTED GLOBAL WARMING CALENDAR

DECEMBER

BEFORE

AFTER

BEFORE

AFTER

© Steve Bell 1989

22·11·2277

23·11·2278

IT'S A DISGRACE!

HERE WE SIT AT THE HUB OF ONE OF THE WORLD'S OLDEST **RODENTOCRACIES**, YET I AM UNABLE TO GET THE **PRIME TIME COVERAGE**.....

....THAT MY CONSTITUENTS IN THE **CRUMBLING SEWERS** OF THE **METROPOLIS** ARE CRYING OUT FOR, SIMPLY BECAUSE THAT BUGGER'S **LEG** IS IN THE WAY! **POINT OF ORDER!!!**

© Steve Bell 1989

DRONE

POINT OF ORDER MR. SQUEAKER SIR!!

ON YOUR BIKE!! I NAME THE MEM- -BER FOR EAST PECKHAM TOILETS!

83

24.11.2279~

OH NO! I'VE BEEN **NAMED**! HERE COMES **BLACKRODENT**!!

GIT OUDA TOWN, EAST PECKHAM TOILETS!!

THIS IS AN **OUTRAGE**!

..THE VERY FABRIC OF OUR **RODENTOCRACY** is **THREATENED** UNLESS I **GAIN** MAXIMUM **MEDIA COVERAGE**! THERE'S ONLY ONE THING FOR IT....

OI!! COME **BACK'ERE**!!

© Steve Bell 1989

I'LL HAVE TO STAGE A **WIGTOP** PROTEST WHERE I'M **GUARANTEED CAMERA TIME** !!

HOLY DOCUDRAMA!! **PISSED-UP**, SEMI-SOMNAMBUAANT MEMBERS ARE **BEATING** EACH OTHER WITH **MACES**...

25.11.2280

..USING PROFANE LANGUAGE, **BARING** THEIR BOTTOMS AND **VOMITING** IN PUBLIC !! WE **CAN'T** SHOW **THIS**! IT'S **AGAINST** THE **LAW**! CUTAWAY TO THE **SPEAKER** !!!

© Steve Bell '89

PHEW !.....OH MY GOD-- WHAT'S **THAT** ??

MAMMY! HOW I **LOVE** YA! HOW I **LOVE** YA!! 'MMM

OR-DAH! **OR-DAH**!

MADEAR OL'MAMMY.... ...AND REMEMBER: PECKHAM'S **TOILETS** ARE A NATIONAL **DISGRACE**!.. **MAMMY**!! **MAMMMY** !!

OR-DAH! **OR-DAH**!! **ORRRR- -DAH**!!

YIBYIBYIB!

KILLER KLARKE

This is the sort of 'getting around the table' that I prefer!

A major **GREASE-OUT** with chips, bangers, runny fried eggs and a couple of **CIGARS**... CHOFF CHOFF **BELCH**...

OOERRR! I'm getting twinges in the ticker!! QUICK! Call an ambulance! —but make sure it's a **REAL ONE!!**

RUMBLE

KRASH

It's alright—you haven't had a **HEART ATTACK**...

...**PRINCIPALLY BECAUSE YOU HAVE NO HEART**, Y' **FAT GIT!!**

29·11·2282

...and now for some **INFORMED COMMENT**...

NEWS

...we go over to a **STRIPY SHIRTED SHIT IN THE CITY**...

...and today's **STRIPY SHIRTED CITY SHIT** is **TONY TURK** at TODDLER WANKTANK + TEASMADE. **TONY:** What's the feeling in the city at the moment?

WELL, BASICALLY WE'RE IN IT FOR THE **MONEY MONEY MONEY**...

...whereas the **AMBULANCE PEOPLE ARE NOT**, therefore as public servants it is their **DUTY** to **ACCEPT WAGE RESTRAINT!**

THANK YOU TONY!

30·11·2284

A STRIPY SHIRTED SHIT IN THE CITY GIVES HIS INFORMED COMMENT:

...THE GOVERNMENT ABSOLUTELY MUST HOLD FIRM ON WAGE SETTLEMENTS OTHER-WISE ALL HELL WILL BREAK LOOSE.....

YOU SEE, THE HEALTH SERVICE IS NOT A PRODUCTIVE INDUSTRY AS SUCH..... ERK!!! I'VE JUST STUCK MY MONT BLANC PEN UP MY NOSE!! AAARRGH!!

QUICK!! CALL AN AMBULANCE! — I MEAN A REAL ONE!! I'M HAEMORRHAGING!! I MAY DIE!! THERE'S BIG MONEY RIDING ON ME!! AAAARRRRGGGHHH!! QUICK! QUICK!!

THANKYOU MY GOOD MAN — YOU'LL BE GLAD TO KNOW THAT BY HELPING ME, YOU'RE HELPING TO GET YOUR NATIONAL ECONOMY BACK ON ITS FEET. PLEASE ACCEPT THIS SMALL TOKEN OF MY ESTEEM!

©Steve Bell 1989—

KILLER KLARKE

GOOD MORNING WORLD!!

PHARRRT

BETTER GET UP I SUPPOSE. F*** OFF CAT!! WHAT'S IN THE NEWS??

FANS ATTACKED BY AMBULANCE BEASTS

ANY BIG-EYED BABY STIFFS I CAN BLAME ON THE AMBULANCE WORKERS? I'LL GET THOSE BASTARDS YET!! PISS OFF, GRANMA! DON'T READ OVER MY SHOULDER!!

KRAK!

I TELL YOU WHAT — FROM NOW ON AS FAR AS THESE SCUMBAG HEALTHWORKERS ARE CONCERNED, IT'S NO MORE MISTER NICE GUY!!

CHOFF

4·12·2287~

IT SAYS HERE WE'RE **DEAD**!!

WE'RE NOT **DEAD** ARE WE?

LARGE AS **LIFE**!!

YODEL-AY-EEE·OOO!!

GRUNT- NO **WAY**!!

BONK

COO

I'M **RESERVING** MY **POSITION** WITH REGARD TO THE ALIVE/ **DEAD** DEBATE, **GLORIA**!!

I'M SO GLAD— EVERYTHING'S **HUNKY DORY** THEN....

HELLO LITTLE **PIGEON**— WHAT **BRINGS** YOU TO THE **SOCIALIST SEABIRDS REPUBLIC** OF **ROCKALL**?

COO! COO!

THAT'S RIGHT—US **GANNETS** ARE STAGING A **COUP**!! YOU **LEFTIES** ARE **ALL WASHED UP**!!

GURK!

GURK!

GURK!

COO! COO!

—©Steve Bell 1989~

GANNET POWER IS SWEEPING AWAY YOU CRAP PENGUINS AND YOUR STAGNANT REGIME!

GURK!

GURK!

5·12·2288~

A **FRESH WIND** IS BLOWING! THE WIND OF FREEDOM, THE WIND OF ENTERPRISE, THE WIND OF GOOD HONEST **GANNET GREED**.....

GURK!

GURK!

GURK!

WE WANT **POLL TAX** WE WANT **PRIVATE FISH** WE WANT **PRIVATE GUANO** WE WANT **PRIVATE SEAWATER** WE WANT **HEREDITARY PEERAGES**!!

GURK!

GURK!

DON'T YOU DUMMIES REALISE?— **SOCIALISM** IS A **DEAD DUCK**!!

GURK

© Steve Bell 1989

88

CONTRARY TO ALL THE SCIENTIFIC EVIDENCE, JOHN SELWYN GUMMER HAS CONTRACTED **MAD COW DISEASE**....

MOOO MOOO!! FOAM FOAM !!! JESUS WANTS ME FOR A SUNBEAM!! MOOOOO!!!

MOOO!! FLAP FLAP!!

..**FOAM SLOBBER DROOL!!!** BUT DON'T WORRY, FOLKS THING AREN'T AS **DISTURBING** AS THEY **LOOK** :

ALL I NEED IS A **SHORT SHARP** BURST OF **RADIATION** , AND : **HEY PRESTO! I'M WHOLESOME AGAIN** !!!

DANGER — RADIO ACTIVE

© Steve Bell 1989

GUMMER!! C'MERE YOU LITTLE **YUMMY!!**

ULP!

YOU'RE SO **GOODY-GOOD** I WANT TO **EAT YOU UP!!** MMMMMM YOU **RIPE JUICY** LITTLE **MORSEL!!**

© Steve Bell 1989

HOW REFRESHINGLY **GREEN** AND **SLIMY** YOU LOOK! TELL ME — ARE YOU **WHOLESOME??**

YES MUM — THE MIRACLE OF **RADIATION** MEANS THAT I AM COMPLETELY **WHOLESOME** WITHIN THE TERMS OF THE "**GREEN FOOD BILL**" AS WELL AS BEING **TEN YEARS** BEYOND MY 'SELL BY' **DATE !!!**

90

THE SEASONALLY ADJUSTED GLOBAL WARMING CALENDAR

JANUARY

94

YOU CAN'T BE SERIOUS— THE **TRIDENT WARHEAD CONTRACT**!! I MEAN— SELLING OUT IS ONE THING....

-15·12·2297-

...BUT **HOW COULD** YOU? AFTER ALL WE'VE STRUGGLED FOR OVER THE YEARS!

RELAX GLORIA!

@Steve Bell 1989

...I'M PLANNING TO MAKE THIS CONTRACT A PARAGON OF **GLOBAL HARMONY**....

HOW SO?

I'M SUBCONTRACTING THE ENTIRE PRODUCTION PACKAGE TO A SMALL FIRM IN **SIBERIA**!!

I'VE JUST BEEN ON TO **REG KIPLING** IN SIBERIA...

YOU DON'T MEAN **REG** IS INVOLVED IN THIS SQUALID SCHEME?

STUNNED

-16·12·2298-

SURE THING. HOW COULD THE HARD-PRESSED **SIBERIAN ECONOMY** TURN DOWN A GUARANTEED HARD CURRENCY EARNER LIKE THE TRIDENT **WARHEAD CONTRACT**?? — I'LL TELL YOU SOMETHING ELSE— THEIR TENDER WAS A FRACTION OF ITS NEAREST RIVAL.....

GORK....

...PLUS THEY GUARANTEE DELIVERY BY AIR, **DIRECT**, ANY TIME WE WANT — WHICH WE DON'T OF COURSE... **FUNNY OLD WORLD**, EH??

© Steve Bell 1989

OH YES..... AND I FORGET TO MENTION THE **£60 MILLION SWEETENER** NO QUESTIONS, NO NAMES, NO PACKDRILL..... THIS IS **CORRUPTION TO END ALL CORRUPTION**!!

HURDBO AND 'CHUCK' HOWE IN

SEND 'EM BACK

-20·12·2301-

I DON'T GET IT, RAMBO-- WHY DO **YOU** OF ALL PEOPLE OBJECT TO US PITCHFORKIN' THESE G**KS BACK TO G**KLAND? WE'RE ON **YOUR SIDE,** GODDAMMIT!!

DA POINT IS **DIS** -- DIS LOOKS **BAD** -- NOT ONLY DAT, IT MAKES **ME** LOOK BAD AND **DAT'S** BAD ON ACCOUNT OF IT'S **BAD** TO **LOOK** BAD!!

©STEVE BELL 1989

BUT RAMBO-- WHAT AM I SUPPOSED TO DO WITH THE G**KS?? **I** DON'T WANT THE G**KS, THE CH**KS DON'T WANT THE G**KS, HELL-- EVEN THE G**KS DON'T WANT THE G**KS!

DAT'S NOT MY PROBLEM!

...DO **YOU** WANT THE G**KS?

HELL NO -- HAVIN' A LOAD O' HANG DOG G**KS HANGIN' AROUND MY OWN BACKYARD'LL MAKES **ME** LOOK REALLY **REALLY** BAD!!

HURDBO RAMBO AND 'CHUCK' HOWE IN

SEND 'EM BACK

-21·12·2302-

RAMBO-- PEOPLE ARE ASKIN' IF WE REALLY GIVE A MONKEY'S FART FOR **HUMAN** RIGHTS!

SURE I CARE!!

THOSE'RE G**KS, BUT YOU SHOW ME SOME **HUMANS** AND I'LL SHOW YOU **HOW MUCH** I CARE.!!

©STEVE BELL 1989

ANYWAY-- AIN'T WE RATHER FORGETTIN' ABOUT THE **CENTRAL ISSUE?** WHAT ABOUT DA RIGHTS OF DA **M.I.A.P.O.W.** s???

BUT RAMBO-- THE MISSING IN ACTION PRISONERS OF WAR DON'T ACTUALLY **EXIST.** THAT WAS A FIGMENT OF A HOLLYWOOD **SCRIPTWRITER'S** IMAGINATION.

YOU SEE-- YOU'RE EVEN DENYIN' THEIR RIGHT TO EXIST! YOU **CRUEL COMMIE** BASTARD! THAT MAKES ME **WEEP!!**

98

100

102

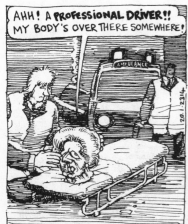

YOU PROFESSIONAL DRIVERS HAVE BEEN SO **SUPERB**...

BASH BASH CLANK

...SO **MYEGNIFICENT**...

...SO **MARVELLOUS** THAT I HAVE DECIDED AT 12 NOON ON THE 30TH...

HORMONO

THOGGEDDA THOGGEDDA THOGGEDDA

CLANK

...TO TAKE TIME OUT TO TELL YOU TO **DROP DEAD** IN AN ESPECIALLY **CARING** VOICE!

IN DARKEST **CHINGFORD**:

CONSERVATIVE CLUB

GIVE 'EM **HELL** ON THE SLANT-EYE QUESTION, NORM — WE CAN'T HAVE 'EM **FLOODING** INTO THE **FATHERLAND**....

INDEED

...SWAMPIN' OUR VERDANT **HEARTLANDS**, THREATENIN' OUR **WAY OF LIFE**, EATIN' THEIR **STINKY FOOD**, WRITIN' BACK TO FRONT AND UPSIDE DOWN...

I WAS IN **H.K.** MYSELF, NORM, AND ALL I EVER GOT FROM JOHNNY SLANT EYE WAS **DUMB INSOLENCE**...

VERY TRUE

...MORNING NOON AND NIGHT: **DUMB INSOLENCE**.... ...IN FACT I THINK WE OUGHT TO CHANGE THE **NAME** OF THIS **CONSTITUENCY**, NORM!

EH?

"**CHING**" FORD SOUNDS DAMNABLY **CHINESE** TO ME....

104

THE SEASONALLY ADJUSTED GLOBAL WARMING CALENDAR

FEBRUARY

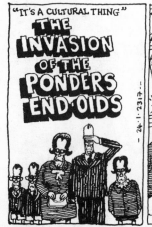

Chingford Sentinel

INFLUX OF UP TO 250000 PONDERS ENDOIDS THREATENS TO SWAMP OUR VERY WAY OF LIFE

— 25·1·2318 —

CRIKEY — I'VE GOT RUDDY **GRAVY** ALL OVER MY TROUSERS, MOTHER!

DON'T WORRY, DADDY — I'LL **IRON IT OFF** FOR YOU IN HALF A TICK!!

— ©Steve Bell 1990 —

WELL MOTHER — LOOKS LIKE THERE'S TROUBLE IN THE **SUDETEN LAND** …. AND THE RISING TIDE OF **PERMISSIVE-NESS** SEEMS SET TO **ENGULF US ALL!!**

I'LL HAVE THIS OFF IN A JIFFY!!

SSSSSSSS

PERMISSIVE THREAT TO FAMILY

… WHICH REMINDS, ME — — I HAVEN'T HAD MY **RUDENESS** YET THIS WEEK, SO UPSTAIRS WITH YOU **P.D.Q.**, MOTHER!!

RIGHTY HO!

—26·1·2319—

Chingford Sentinel

'I'M NO RACIST — — I object to any massive influx of Ponders Endoids on purely cultural grounds' —CHINGFORD NAZI

SEE WHAT'S ON **TELLY**, DADDY

THERE'S BALLY GRAND **HOPERA** AND A LOT OF PINKISH SEXUALLY PERMISSIVE **SO-CALLED DRAMA** — NOTHING FOR THE LIKES OF US, MOTHER!

SSSLLLPP   SSSLLLPP

SWITCH IT ON ANYWAY — — THERE MIGHT BE A NICE **TRAVEL PROGRAMME** OR A **QUIZ SHOW** ON LATER

RIGHTY HO!

KLIK

©Steve Bell 1990

NEXT ON ONE — THE FIRST IN A BRAND NEW SERIES OF **'FUCK'EM IF THEY CAN'T TAKE A JOKE'**

!!!   !!!

CRASH

108

27·1·2320

INFLUX OF THE PONDERS ENDOIDS

...SO YOU SEE CHILDREN, YOUR **AVERAGE CHINESE** DOES NOT APPRECIATE WESTERN CONCEPTS LIKE **DEMOCRACY**..... IT'S ALL IN THE **BONE STRUCTURE**, Y'KNOW...

SSSSSELLLPP

SSSLLPP

...THEY WOULDN'T KNOW WHAT TO DO WITH A VOTE IF YOU GAVE IT TO THEM ALL **TOMORROW**. THEY'RE JUST **NOT READY FOR IT**. YOUR AVERAGE CHINAMAN THINKS AND ACTS AS PART OF A MASS. THAT IS WHY THEY ALL **LOOK THE SAME**...

© Steve Bell 1990

..PERHAPS, GIVEN SEVERAL MILLENNIA THEY MIGHT EVOLVE THE **RUGGED NO-NONSENSE INDIVIDUALISM** LIKE WHAT WE HAD IN **PONDERS END** AND HAVE BROUGHT WITH US TO OUR NEW HOMELAND HERE IN **CHINGFORD**.

DEPORT THE YACHT PEOPLE

HOLLOW CHEEK DOME HEADS OUT

KEEP CHINGFORD PURPLE

SAVE OUR CULTURE

TEA SLURPING BISCUIT CRUNCHERS OUT

NO MORE FUNNY LINGO

29·1·2321

© Steve Bell 1990

HELP! I'M BEING **KIDNAPPED** BY TWO YUPPIES!!

113

IN THE SNUG OF THE LOCAL POLARIS:

ANNIHILATION STREET

DOIN' ANYTHIN' TONIGHT Y' BIG BRASSY BELTER??

AH'M WASHIN' ME URR

ALL THIS **RADIO-ACTIVE** LEAKING IS PLAYING MERRY 'ELL WI' ME **BIO-RHYTHMS**!!

CHEEKY BOOGER! THURR'S **NO LEAKS** ON THIS TUB!

Y' MEAN — EVERYTHING'S UNDER CONTROL, THE FLEET IS FULLY OPERATIONAL AND THURR'S **NO THREAT** TO THE THREAT??

THAT'S RIGHT CHOOK!

SO WHY'RE WE ALL PARKED UP IN SALFORD THEN? IS IT 'OLIDAY TIME???

SHUT IT CLEVERDICK!

POOT

© Steve Bell 1990

ANNIHILATION STREET

'EY KID - GORRA **YTS** PROJECT FOR YOU! NIP DOWN T' ROAD AND BUY US A ROLL O' **STICKY TAPE**. ME NUCLEAR SUBMARINE NEEDS MENDIN' — 'ERE'S 20p!!

'ANG ON - STICKY TAPE COSTS 50p!!

DRIZZLES FIERCE T' DAY

'APPEN

I MAY BE **YOUNG**, BUT I'M NOT **THICK**

ANY MORE LIP AN' YOU'LL GERRA **THICK EAR**, Y' CHEEKY MONKEY!!

IT'S WORSE IN OLDHAM Y' KNOW!

ANYROAD - 'OW COME YER NOT AT **SCHOOL**??

IT'S **SHUT**, AN' THURR'S **NO ROOF** AN' **NO TEACHERS** 'COS MY GOVERNMENT SPENDS £21·2 BILLION ON DEFENCE AND ONLY £5·7 BILLION ON EDUCATION

LISTEN 'ERE **SMARTYPANTS** — THAT SORT O' **WHINGEIN' CLAPTRAP** IN'T ON 'T NATIONAL CURRICULUM, SO JUST **SHUT IT** WHILE I SMACK YER LEG!!

POOT!

© Steve Bell 1990

HELLO... I'VE BEEN SELECTED BY A LEADING ADVERTISING AGENT BECAUSE I LOOK LIKE A NORMAL, WORRIED SORT OF **C2-ISH PERSON.** YOU MIGHT HAVE SEEN THESE ADS...

Don't miss out *Act **now** and you could **pay** less* Community Charge *in April*

"PAY LESS" THEY SAY.... ..BUT I DON'T PAY RATES **DIRECTLY** AT THE MOMENT – I PAY THEM VIA THE **LANDLORD** AS PART OF THE **RENT**....

COME **APRIL 1st** I BECOME RESPONSIBLE FOR PAYING **'THE CHARGE'** FOR EACH OF MY 18 YEAR OLD TWINS AND FOR MY FATHER-IN-LAW. THAT MEANS WE'RE GOING TO HAVE TO FIND SOMETHING CONSERVATIVELY IN THE REGION OF **£1200** PER ANNUM....

..OR **£23** PER WEEK. I TRIED ASKING THE **LANDLORD**, BUT HE JUST **LAUGHED** IN MY FACE. THAT'S WHY I'M RIPPING UP NEWSPAPERS AND DUNKING THEM IN PIPING HOT WATER TO MAKE A NOURISHING ECONOMICAL **SOUP**.....

I'M A **LANDLORD.** THESE CUFFLINKS COST ME **100K.** FABERGÉ. I'M A **CONNOISSEUR**

Don't mi... Act now an... could pay les... Community Cha... in April

GOT SOME **VERY FINE** PROPERTIES; GOT A LOT OF NASTY PROPERTIES; FULL OF **SCUMBAG POOR TYPES.** A LOT OF THESE SCUMBAGS PAY **RATES** AS PART OF THE **RENT**....

COME **APRIL 1st**; NO MORE RATES; SCUMBAGS HAVE GOTTA PAY **POLL TAX** FOR **THEMSELVES,** AND SINCE I'M NOT LOWERING THE RENT THAT MAKES FOR A NICE LITTLE **BONUS**...

...I THINK I'LL BUY MYSELF **ANOTHER SET OF CUFFLINKS**....

115

I'M A **SCOTS STEREOTYPE**. I WIS LOOKIN' AT THE **POLL TAX ADS** IN YOUR ENGLISH PAPERS, AN' I'VE JUST **ONE THING** TAE SAY:

Don't Act now could pay Community in April

16.2.2337

SPEAKIN' AS A RESPONSIBLE PERSON FACED WI' A POLL TAX BILL O' OWER **TWA THOOSAND POONDS** (THERE'S **SEVEN ADULTS** IN THIS HOOSE) AFTER HAVIN' PAID RATES A' THESE YEARS AS **PART O' THE RENT** TAE OOR LANDLORD MISTER McHOOGSTRATEN, AN' GETTIN' **NAE REBATE**, I'D LIKE TAE SAY THIS:

THE COMMUNITY PANIC NOW

DINNA PANIC!! I HAUVNAE PAID A **PENNY** O' POLL TAX A' YEAR, AN' THERE'S NIGH ON A **MILLION** IN SCOTLAND LIKE ME — AN' THAT'S OOT O' 3.7 MILLION WHO'RE ELIGIBLE TAE PAY THE BUGGER.... ..**THEY CAN'T** PROSECUTE US A'!!!!

Don't miss out Act now and you could pay less Community Char..

NOW DOGS

...SO JUST THINK HOW MANY THERE'LL BE IN **ENGLAND AND WALES!!** C'MON YOU COONCILS! TELL THIS GOVERNMENT TAE **SHOVE THE WHOLE SCHEME UP THEIR AIRSES** WHERE IT BELONGS !!!

© Steve Bell '90

HEY! WHERE'S YOUR **POLL TAX**?

I AIN'T PAYIN'!

19.2.2338

WHAT D'YOU MEAN —**YOU AIN'T PAYIN'**??

I AIN'T PAYIN' ON ACCOUNT OF IT'S **OBSCENE**, IT'S **EVIL**, IT'S GONNA DRIVE PEOPLE **NUTS**...

© Steve Bell 1990

YESSIR, IT'S NASTY, IT'S **POISONOUS**, IT'S CAUSIN' **MAYHEM** ...

..IN FACT, THE WHOLE SCHEME IS ABOUT AS MUCH USE TO MANKIND AS A **MAD COW PIE** !!!

BLANKS TO OLROD

117

...SO I SAID TO HIM: "I THINK THE HON. GENTLEMAN POSSIBLY TAKES HIS **INSTRUCTIONS** FROM THE **A.N.C.**"

YIS, YIS, IXCELLÉNT!

THAT GOT THE **TERRORÍST STOOGE**, I CAN TELL YOU!

HO HO HO! THET'S A **GOOD** ONE, MEGGIE!

THESE PEOPLE ARE SO WEAK AND HYPOCRITICAL

THEY'RE JUST **TIRRORISTS** WITHOUT THE **BUM** AND THE **BILLET**, MEG...

...NOW HERE IS YOUR **PROGRÉMME FOR TODAY** — WE WOULD LIKE YOU TO ATTECK THE **MEDIA** FOR SHOWING ALL THIS **TIRRIBLE VIO-LENCE** ON YOUR T.V. SCREENS. IT WOULD BE VERY HENDY IF YOU COULD SECURE MORE COVERAGE OF THE **CARING SIDE** OF THE **SETH IFRICAN POLICEMAN**; TALK UP THE NEED FOR **CERROTS** RATHER THAN **STICKS**; A SETH IFRICAN POLICEMAN CAN INFLICT A SURPRISING RANGE OF **INJURIES** WITH A **CERROT**......

MMMM.. UH HUH... YAH..YAH... MMMM

MARGARET! WHAT ABOUT MY **SOUTH AFRICAN INVESTMENTS**?

DON'T WORRY DENIS....

...ANY SANCTIONS AGAINST INVESTMENT ARE ENTIRELY **VOLUNTARY**, AND YOU KNOW **MY** FEELINGS: GO RIGHT AHEAD......

...THE TIME HAS COME TO SPARE THE **STICK** AND APPLY THE **CARROT**. WHAT WERE YOU THINKING OF INVESTING IN??

IT'S AN **ALL NEW GIANT RACIAL THEME PARK** CONCEPT. THEY'RE CALLING IT "**LAAGERLAND**" IT'LL INCLUDE A GIANT FULL-COLOUR FIBREGLASS STATUE OF **YOU**, MARGARET, AND ONE OF THAT GERMAN CHAP WITH THE MOUSTACHE....

118

THE SEASONALLY ADJUSTED GLOBAL WARMING CALENDAR

MARCH

121

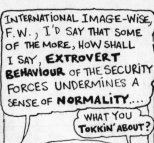

122

126

16-3-2355 —

WHAT'S THIS? EVEN **MORE DIRT** ON THE N.U.M?? **EXCELLENT! EXCELLENT!!**

YES, BOSS

...NOT ONLY DO WE HAVE LINKS TO THE **EVIL EMPIRE**, THERE IS ALSO MENTION OF A SINISTER **'MR BIG'**

OU, Q. TWITCH TWITCH —)

THIS MAN APPARENTLY OPERATED A SHADY **VANITY PUBLISHING HOUSE** FOR ALL THE MOST **CORRUPT DICTATORS** IN OLD-STYLE EASTERN EUROPE!!

WE MUST **EXPOSE THIS MAN** FOR WHAT HE IS!!

IT'S **YOU** Y'FAT GIT!!

MR BIG BOB — THIS IS YO... LIF...

© Steve Bell '90

17-3-2356 —

ARE YOU TRYING TO **MAKE FUN** OF ME??!? DO YOU REALISE I AM **MORE** THAN A MERE BUSINESS **MAGNATE** AND PRESS BARON....

....I AM A **WAR HERO!!** DO YOU REALISE THAT I AM THE MAN WHO SINGLE HANDEDLY ATE HIS WAY BACK FROM BEHIND GERMAN LINES DURING THE **BATTLE OF THE BULGE**....

BOOM

CHOFF CHOFF

...I AM THE MAN WHO INVENTED THE **GORBACHEV REFORMS** THAT ARE NOW SWEEPING EASTERN EUROPE! I AM THE ARCHETYPAL **SOCIALIST CAPITALIST!**....

© Steve Bell 1990 —

...I AM THE MOST **ENORMOUS THING** TO HIT EUROPEAN POLITICS SINCE **CHARLES THE FAT** DIED IN **888**! I AM **WISDOM**! I AM **TEMPERANCE**! I AM **MODESTY**! I AM **CHASTITY**!!

FORGET MILITANT, NEIL — I THINK IT'S TIME WE **DISTANCED OURSELVES** FROM THIS CHARACTER!!

THE MAD COWS

You can call me GEORGE III

22.3.2359

YES, IT WAS A **TOUGH**, BORING BUDGET, BORING IN ITS **TOUGHNESS**, YET SOMEHOW TOUGH IN ITS BOREDOM...

I'M SORRY..... DID YOU SAY SOMETHING?

I SUPPOSE I'VE ALWAYS BEEN A BIT BORING. I'VE ALWAYS FELT THAT **YOU** SOMEHOW SET A **GLOBAL STANDARD** IN THIS FIELD?

SORRY...I...I BEG YOUR PARDON?

Y'KNOW, WHAT I ALWAYS SAY TO MARGARET IS THIS: WHEN THE **GOING** GETS **TOUGH**, THE **DUFFS** GET **BORING**....

ZZZZZZZ

© Steve Bell 1990

ZZZZZZZ   ZZZZZZ

ZZZZZZ   ZZZZZ

The MAD COWS

22.3.2360

HEY! LOOK AT **THIS**!! IT SAYS HERE KINNOCK IS **ON THE RUN**....

© Steve Bell 1990

..HE'S MISSED HIS **CHANCE** ON THE **POLL TAX**. HE'S BEEN **EXPOSED** BY THE UGLY FACE OF **MILITANT EXTREMIST VIOLENCE**....

YOU WHAT?

TOP TORIES ARE SET TO **FIGHT BACK** AND SWEEP TO VICTORY.

IS THAT THE **DAILY MAIL** BY ANY CHANCE?

IT'S UNBELIEVABLE SOME OF THE THINGS YOU'RE **EXPECTED** TO **SWALLOW** THESE DAYS....

LET'S BE **POSITIVE** ABOUT THE **COMMUNITY CHARGE**!

WITH THE **BRILLIANT ARCHITECT** OF THE SCHEME AND HIS PERFORMING **RATS** AND **GUINEA PIGS**

THINK OF THE **PRINCIPLE** BEHIND IT: AT LAST COUNCILS WILL BE **TRULY ACCOUNTABLE**! THIS EXPERIMENT SHOWS YOU **HOW**....

SORRY PAL — THE **RENT** ON YOUR CAGE IS GOING **UP 20%** AND YOUR COMMUNITY CHARGE HAS BEEN SET AT **500 VOLTS**!

CONGRETULATIONS! THE RENT ON YOUR CAGE IS GOING UP **20%**, AND YOUR **COMMUNITY** CHARGE HAS BEEN SET AT ONLY **190 VOLTS**!!

©Steve Bell 1990

AH SEE YOU! TOORRY BASSTARD!!

IN ORDER TO **SCIENTIFICALLY VINDICATE** THE PRINCIPLE AND PRACTICE OF COMMUNITY CHARGE I HAVE FIXED **ELECTRODES** TO THE GUINEA PIG'S **GENITALIA**....

SORRY, PAL — I'M JUST OBEYIN' ORDERS. YOUR COMMUNITY CHARGE HAS BEEN SET AT **500 VOLTS**. DON'T TRY AND **DODGE IT**!

©Steve Bell 90

CONGRETULATIONS! THENKS TO CONSERVATIVE **THRIFT**, YOUR CHARGE IS ONLY **4.50 VOLTS**!

AH SEE YOU! TOORRY BASSTARD!!

THE SEASONALLY ADJUSTED GLOBAL WARMING CALENDAR

APRIL

LET'S BE **POSITIVE** ABOUT COMMUNITY CHARGE!! THINK OF THE **SIMPLICITY**: EVERYONE GETS THE SAME CHARGE, AS DEMONSTRATED BY THESE **EXPERIMENTAL RATS** AND **GUINEA PIGS**...

-28·3·2365-

SORRY PAL, YOU GET **375** VOLTS

SORRY PAL- YOU GET **310** VOLTS!

SMILE! THANKS TO CONSERVATIVE THRIFT, YOU GET **450** VOLTS

SORRY COLLEAGUE- YOU GET **478** VOLTS

SORRY PAL- YOU GET **543** VOLTS

SORRY, PAL- YOU GET **292** VOLTS!

ZZZZZZZT FLASH BANG ZZAP

WE SEE YOU! TORY OILSLICK!!

©Steve Bell 1990

LET'S BE **POSITIVE** ABOUT THE 'CHARGE': IT'S SO **SIMPLE** AND EASY TO ADMINISTER. WITNESS THIS **PRACTICAL DEMONSTRATION** IN THE FIELD....

-29·3·2366-

'SCUSE ME PAL- HAVE YOU SEEN **ONE MILLION GUINEA PIGS** GOING THIS WAY BY ANY CHANCE ??

WHO WANTS TAE KNOW ?

GOT A WEE PRESENT FOR THEM: THEIR **300 VOLT COMMUNITY CHARGE**

WHAT DID THEY **LOOK LIKE**?

SMALL, FURRY, 'BOUT **THIS LONG**.... ....SOME O' THEM MIGHT HA' BEEN WEARING **TAM O' SHANTERS**

ABOUT **ONE MILLION** OF 'EM, YOU SAY?? HMMMM

©Steve Bell 1990

SORRY PAL- DOESNAE RING ANY BELLS

OCH, SHITE!

135

AH'M **SHERRIFF** ROOND HERE, AN' AH'M LOOKIN' FER **ONE MILLION** DISSIDENT, COMMUN-ITY-CHARGE-AVOIDING **GUINEA PIGS**!!

HOWDY

30·3·2367

IT'S MA' SOLEMN DUTY TAE **DISCIPLINE** THESE NAUGHTY WEE BEASTS!

WHAT'RE YE GONNA **DO** WITH'EM WHEN YE FIND'EM??

I'LL **SELL OFF** THE CONTENTS O' THEIR **FILTHY WEE CAGES**, ITEM BY ITEM!

HOW LONG D'YE RECKON THAT'LL TAKE??

'BOUT **EIGHTY YEARS**— MIND YOU, AH'VE GOT TAE **FIND** THE BUGGERS FIRST!!

©Steve Bell 1990

·31·3·2368·

YOU ARE OUR INSPIRATION, MA'AM!

HELLAY TEAM!!! READY FOR THE **BIG DAY**?

HMMM.... LET'S SEE— TOMORROW THE **SHIT** REALLY HITS THE **FAN** ON **ALL FRONTS**...OR IS THAT MIXING MY METAPHORS?

YOUR SPEECH IS AN EXAMPLE TO US ALL, MA'AM!

THERE ARE ALL THE **SCHOOLS** WE'RE PLUNGING INTO FINANCIAL CHAOS; **HOSPITALS**; **HOUSING**; **MASS BANKRUPTCIES** THANKS TO THE NEW **BUSINESS RATE**; AND ON TOP OF ALL THAT **THE POLL TAX**!!! WHAT A CONSUMMATE **COCK UP**!!!

©Steve Bell 1990

SERVES 'EM RIGHT FOR VOTING FOR ME, **APRIL FOOOLS**!!!

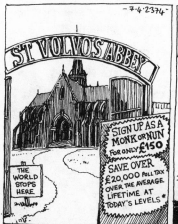

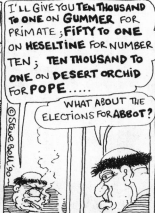

DID YOU HEAR THE ONE ABOUT THE 'ILLEGAL' STATE SUBSIDY FOR THE CHANNEL TUNNEL LINK?

I ♥ DIESEL FUMES

CHILD ON BOARD

TO GET IT PAST THE D.T.I. THEY HAD TO DISGUISE IT....

I ♥ URBAN SNARL UPS

©Steve Bell '90

...AS A NEW NERVE GAS DELIVERY SYSTEM FROM PORTON DOWN TO BAGHDAD VIA SWANLEY AND SEVENOAKS!

I ♥ CARBON MONOXIDE

CHILD ON BOARD

REG...THIS YIS MADNESS!

I'M GREEN AS A WHISTLE

26·4·2384

"CYCLING HOLIDAY YIN HOME COUNTIES TO VYISIT OLD HAUNTS" - PAH!!

LAGER LAGER LAGER LAGER

YIS STRICTLY FOR THE BIRDS, REG...

YES! LOOK!! A SKYLARK!

ANOTHER LOAD OF INTERCONTINENTAL BALLISTIC SURFBOARDS FOR THE IRAQI TOURIST BOARD

dti

I'M THINKING MORE OF THE FLAT ONES EMBEDDED YIN TARMAC, REG....

DTI ARMOURED KITCHENS

©Steve Bell '90

143

Zis is MOST IRREGULAR—
—YOU SAY YOU VILL PUT ZE
NUCLEAR VASTE IN A CUPBOARD
UNDER ZE STAIRS? MEIN GOTT!!

AT LEAST WE KNOW
WHERE WE'RE PUTTING IT—
—BRITISH NUCLEAR FUELS
HAVEN'T GOT A CLUE!!

UNDER THE
RUG

VELL, I DON'T
KNOW...

COME ON! YOU
CAN'T BUCK THE MARKET!
HAVE WE GOT A DEAL OR
HAVE WE GOT A DEAL??

THE BACK OF
MY SOCK
DRAWER!

STUFF IT IN
MY FAVOURITE
ARMCHAIR!

FACE FACTS — A SOCK
DRAWER IN DOCKLAND
IS AS SAFE AS ANYTHING
B.N.F.L. HAS SUGGESTED,
PLUS OUR SCHEME HAS
AN ADDED BONUS...

© Steve Bell 90

....WE'RE NOT GOING TO
FART ABOUT WITH IT, MASSIVE-
LY INCREASE ITS TOTAL
VOLUME AND CLAIM WE'RE
"RE-PROCESSING" IT.
ONCE WE PUT IT IN THE
SOCK DRAWER IT STAYS
PUT AND STAYS THE SAME
SIZE!!

I NEED TO SINK
ABOUT ZIS

— 2. 5. 2389 —

THE INCREDIBLE
WOMBLEWOMEN

— 3. 5. 2390 —

CRIKEY! WHAT HAVE YOU
JUST WOMBLED UP
LADY P.??

LOOKS LIKE
A DISTRESSED FORMER
RATEPAYER!!

I SAY! YOU'VE JUST GIVEN
ME AN IDEA FOR A FABULOUS
VOTE WINNING SLOGAN —
— IT CAN'T FAIL!

— © Steve Bell 1990 —

DON'T VOTE LABOUR
OR WE'LL DIG UP
YOUR GRANNY
AND COUNT HER
AS A CONSERVATIVE
VOTER BY DEFAULT

'Cons cost less'

THANKS TO CHRIS BAINBRIDGE

...I'M SUMMONING YOU TO A TOTAL CRISIS MANAGEMENT **POWER BREAKFAST!** BE THERE!!!

AND SO:

WHO PUT THIS **REVOLVER** IN MY BOWL? WHAT EXACTLY IS THE MEANING OF THIS??

ER..... DO THE DECENT THING

POWER BRAN BOLT!

IRON RIVET 'N' HONEY SNAK

AT A CRISIS POWER BREAKFAST IN THE BUNKER.....

WHO HAS BEEN LEAVING THESE **CRYPTIC MESSAGES?** WHAT AM I SUPPOSED TO DO WITH THIS **REVOLVER?**

THE DECENT THING

WHY IS THERE A SYRINGE LOADED WITH **STRYCHNINE** FLOATING IN THE **MILK** JUG????

YOUR TIME IS UP

KLANG

WHO WROTE "**PISS OFF AND DIE**" IN FOOT HIGH LETTERS ON MY **STRATEGIC BLACKBOARD???**

PISS OFF AND DIE

IS ONE OF YOU TRYING TO **TELL ME SOMETHING??**

146

THE SEASONALLY ADJUSTED GLOBAL WARMING CALENDAR

MAY

FOOLS!! DO YOU THINK I WOULD ABANDON THE FIELD AT THIS **CRITICAL STAGE** IN OUR HISTORY? I DIDN'T INVITE YOU TO THIS **POWER BREAKFAST** IN ORDER TO SIMPLY ADMIT **DEFEAT!!**

DO YOU REALISE THAT AT THIS VERY MOMENT OUR **EARLY WARNING SYSTEMS** ARE **GROUNDED** AS A RESULT OF THE **SHACKLETON CRASH??**

DO YOU NOT UNDERSTAND??? **RED HORDES** ARE POISED TO INVADE AT **ANY SECOND**... —IN FACT— HERE THEY COME **NOW!!** THEY'RE DISGUISED AS **BAKED BEANS!!!**

THANK THE **LORD** ONE OF YOU GENTLEMEN HAD THE PRESENCE OF MIND TO LEAVE THIS **LOADED REVOLVER** IN MY CORNFLAKE BOWL **!!!**

BLAMMA BLAMMA

THE CRISIS-MANAGEMENT **POWER BREAKFAST** CONTINUES :

THE QUESTION IS — HOW DOES ONE SURVIVE THE PRESENT **POPU-LARITY TROUGH SCENARIO**??... ...GIVE ME THE SHREDDED **RUST'N'RAISIN SNAX**, HOWE!!

ER...NO

DAMMIT — WHO PUT THIS **TIN OPENER, GRENADE** AND **STICK OF DYNAMITE** IN THE CEREAL BOX ??

I JUST WANT TO SAY **THREE THINGS**, MA'AM : **PUBLIC RELATIONS**, **PUBLIC REL-ATIONS** AND **PUBLIC RELATIONS !!**

YOU'RE TALKING MY KIND OF LANGUAGE !!

BUGGER THE **PUBLIC** AND BRING IN YOUR **RELATIONS** IT'S TIME TO DO A **KING FAHD** OF SAUDI ARABIA, MA'AM **!!**

RELATIONS?? I WOULDN'T TRUST 'EM AS FAR AS I COULD THROW 'EM!

CLARKE— AFTER PROLONGED CONSIDERATION AT A RECENT POWER BREAKFAST,— WE'VE DECIDED TO PROVIDE YOU WITH A PERSONAL IMAGE ADVISOR.....

IT'S AN HONOUR TO MEET WITH YOU

11·5·2397

SO WHAT'S THE WORD THEN ??

THE WORD IS: LOSE WEIGHT AND STOP LOSING YOUR TEMPER !!

YOU *@☆*!!@☀ BASTARD !!!!

COOL IT— I'M ONLY TELLING IT LIKE IT IS, FATS!

I ATE THE CHEEKY SWINE! SERVES HIM BLOODY WELL RIGHT !!

BURRRP

© Steve Bell 1990

AH... WADDINGTON— I'D LIKE TO INTRODUCE YOU TO YOUR PERSONAL IMAGE ADVISOR...

12·5·2398

...HE'S VERY KINDLY VOLUN-TEERED HIS SERVICES AS A SYMPATHETIC PERSON IN THE MEDIA. I'D LIKE YOU TO LISTEN TO WHAT HE'S GOT TO SAY

HRRMMMPH.... ...WELL?? WHAT DO YOU WANT ME TO DO TO IMPROVE MY "IMAGE"?

© Steve Bell 1990

KEEP YOUR MOUTH SHUT AND PUT THIS PAPER BAG OVER YOUR HEAD !!!

150

154

I'VE BEEN THINKING — MY LIFESTYLE'S BEEN GETTING A LITTLE **HECTIC** LATELY..... I NEED TO GET BACK **IN TOUCH** WITH MYSELF....

UH HUH YAH!

... I NEED TO GET BACK IN TOUCH WITH THE **PLANET**. I'M TAKING THE **MERCEDES** UP TO **SCOTLAND**....

UH HUH MMMM... YAH...

...I NEED TO SPEND A LITTLE TIME AT MY SHITHOUSE IN THE GLENS

WE ALL HAVE THIS NEED IN US TO **GET CLOSE TO NATURE!**

...THAT'S RIGHT — WE HAVE TO GET CLOSE ENOUGH TO BE ABLE TO SEE THE **WHITES OF ITS EYES!**

YAH HAHA!

KLIK

YAY! UP HERE I FEEL MORE **IN TOUCH**, MORE **IN TUNE**, MORE **ALIVE!!**

WHAT'S THIS? SOME KIND OF RARE **SWAMP ORCHID**? THAT DESERVES **BOTH BARRELS!**

BLAM!

OSPREYS AT TWELVE O'CLOCK: I'LL **GET IN TOUCH** WITH THEM RIGHT AWAY!!

BAM BAM

HEEEY!!! THERE'S A REALLY WEIRD LOOKING BIRD WITH REALLY **STIFF PINK WINGS!** YOU DON'T SEE MANY OF **THEM** ABOUT!!!

...SORRY, YOUR ROYAL HIGHNESS —FOR A MINUTE I MISTOOK YOU FOR AN ENDANGERED SPECIES!

THAT'S QUITE ALRIGHT— —I'M JUST TALKING TO THIS TREE HERE ABITE THE APPALLING MAN-MADE WASTELAND CONFRONTING US ALL ON THIS PLANET

TREE? I DON'T SEE ANY TREE!

I WAS TELLING IT THAT THIS PART OF THE WORLD, SUTHERLAND, USED TO BE FULL OF AUTHENTIC HIGHLAND TYPES....

— ©Steve Bell 1990 —

...UNTIL THE BRITISH ARISTOCRACY DECIDED TO SHIP 'EM ORFF TO THE COLONIES, REPLACE 'EM WITH SHEEP AND DEER AND EXTERMINATE ALL FORMS OF COMPETING WILDLIFE. THASE BINDERS HAVE A LOT TO ANSWER FOR !!

DEMMIT, WE CAN'T GO ON DESPOLIATING OUR HERITAGE THE WAY WE HAVE BEEN. WE'VE GOT TO STAND UP FOR THE ELEPHANTS IN THE TREES....

26.5.2409

WE'VE GOT TO BE KIND TO OUR FELLAY CREATURES..... PEOPLE IN GREEN HIZES SHOULDN'T FIRE SHOTGUNS...... ....OH MY GOD !!...

© Steve Bell '90

...IT'S THE HEREDITARY TRIGGER FINGER !! IT'S STARTING TO ITCH! NNNGGGHH! NNNNNGGH!! I CAN'T STAND IT !!!

THROB TWITCH

GIVE ME THAT GUN! I MUST HAVE SPORT NOW!!

156

159